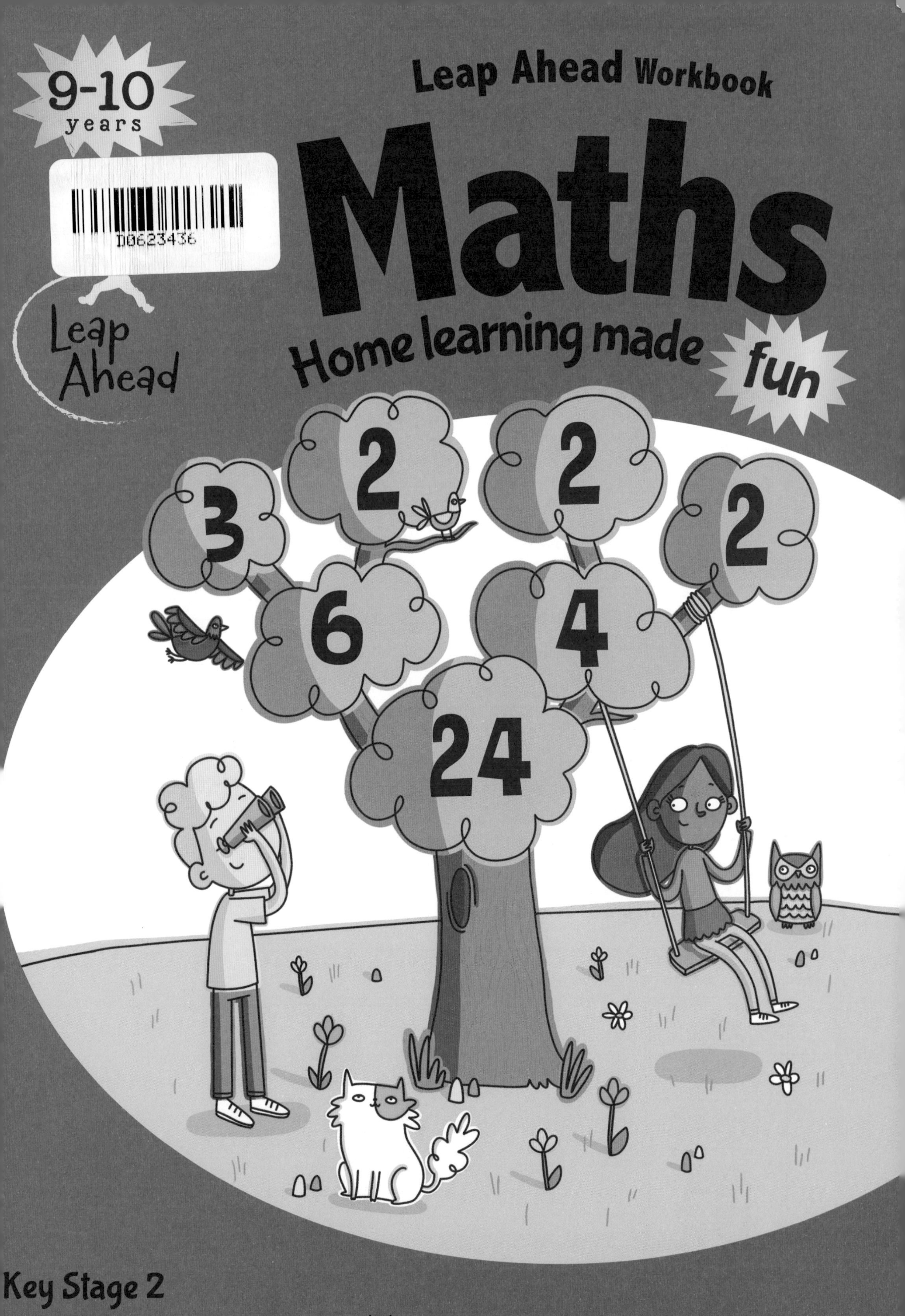
9-10
years
Leap Ahead Workbook
Maths
Home learning made fun
Leap Ahead
3
2
2
2
6
4
24
Key Stage 2
igloo

Big numbers

Jamie's family are thinking of moving house and have narrowed their search down to these houses.

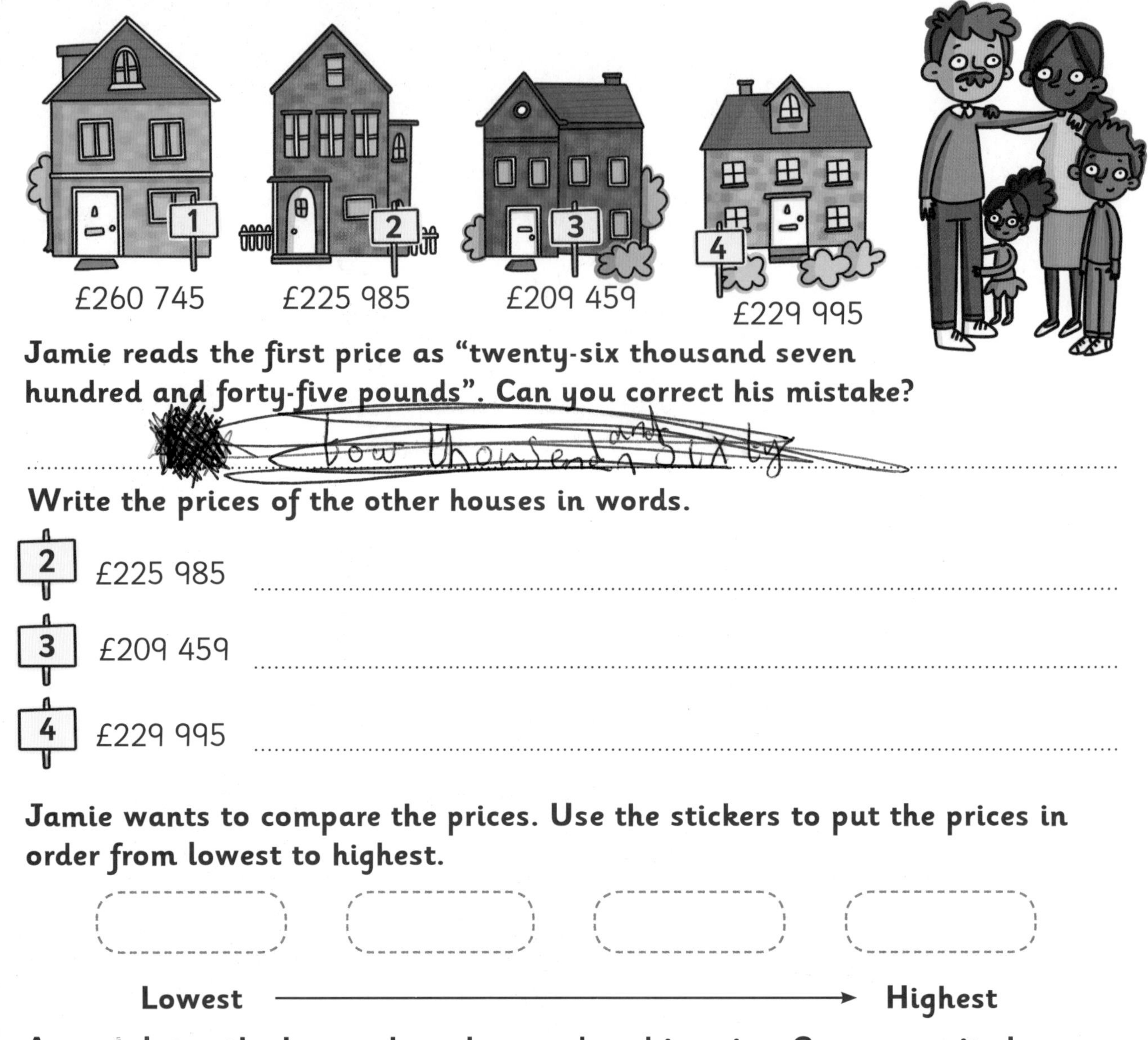

Jamie reads the first price as "twenty-six thousand seven hundred and forty-five pounds". Can you correct his mistake?

....

Write the prices of the other houses in words.

2 £225 985 ....

3 £209 459 ....

4 £229 995 ....

Jamie wants to compare the prices. Use the stickers to put the prices in order from lowest to highest.

Lowest → Highest

A week later, the houses have been reduced in price. Can you write how much each house was reduced by?

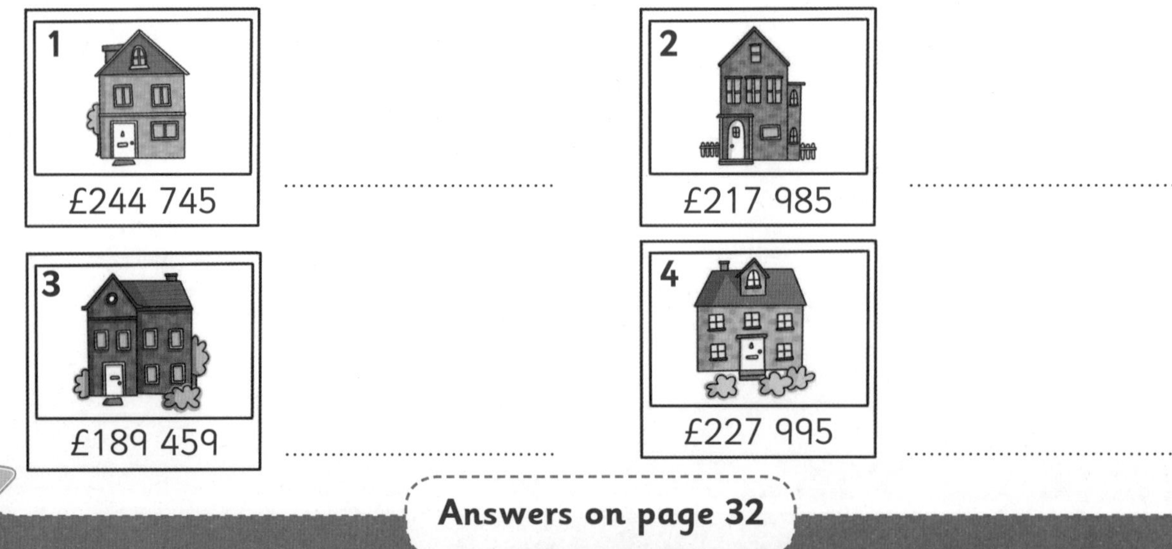

Answers on page 32

Decimal numbers

The family are considering how close each house is to the local school. The distances in kilometres are written on the map.

Jamie says that house 2 is closest because it has the fewest decimal places. Mum says this isn't true. Can you explain to Jamie why?

....

Use stickers to put the houses in order of their distance from the school.

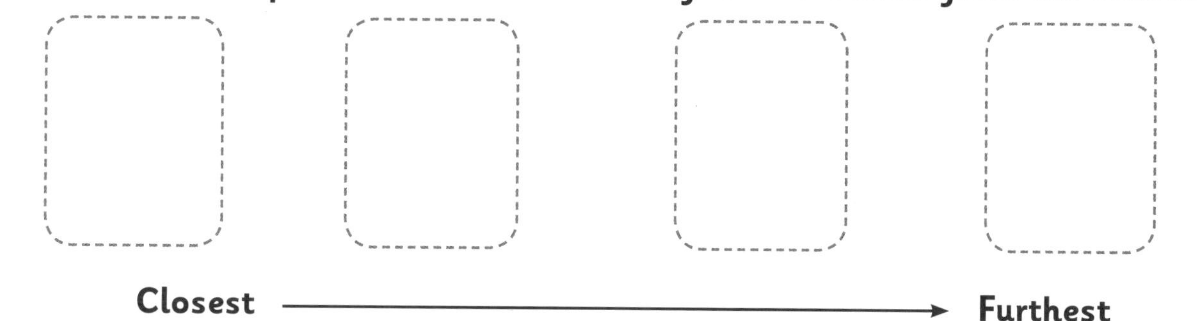

Closest ⟶ Furthest

Jamie then works out how far each house is from his friend's house. Circle the one that is closest.

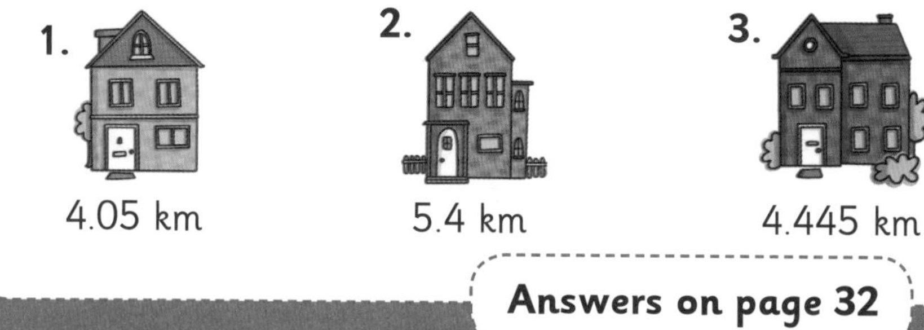

Answers on page 32

PARENT TIP: Write some whole numbers up to 1 million or some decimal numbers with up to 3 decimal places on pieces of paper. Turn them over in a pile. Play "Higher or lower", taking turns to guess whether the next number turned over will be higher or lower than the last.

Multiplying and dividing by 10, 100 and 1000

Callum is working at a pop concert, checking fans' tickets at the door.

1000 fans come through each of the 23 doors. How many fans are at the concert altogether?

....

Later, Callum sells merchandise. Mugs come in boxes of 10, T-shirts come in boxes of 100 and keyrings come in boxes of 1000. Callum works out how many of each he's sold by multiplying the number of boxes he opened by the number in a box. Complete his calculations for him below.

How many mugs in 342 boxes?

342 x 10 = ...

How many boxes makes 7500 keyrings?

.... x 1000 = 7500

How many boxes has Callum opened when he's sold 2400 T-shirts?

100 x .... = ...

He also sells 3000 programmes from 30 boxes. How many programmes come in a box?

.... x 30 = 3000

The next night, Callum helps in the food kiosk. He wants to know how much money the concert makes for every 10, 100 and 1000 items sold. He makes a table to record his workings. Can you help him complete it?

	x1	x10	x100	x1000
Fizzy drinks	£1.99		£199	
Portion of chips	£2.30	£23		
Burgers				£3500
Popcorn	£2.05			
Chocolate bars			£95	

Answers on page 32

Callum is wondering how to measure different items around the kiosk. What unit of measure would he use to measure the following items? Use stickers to match them with the correct unit.

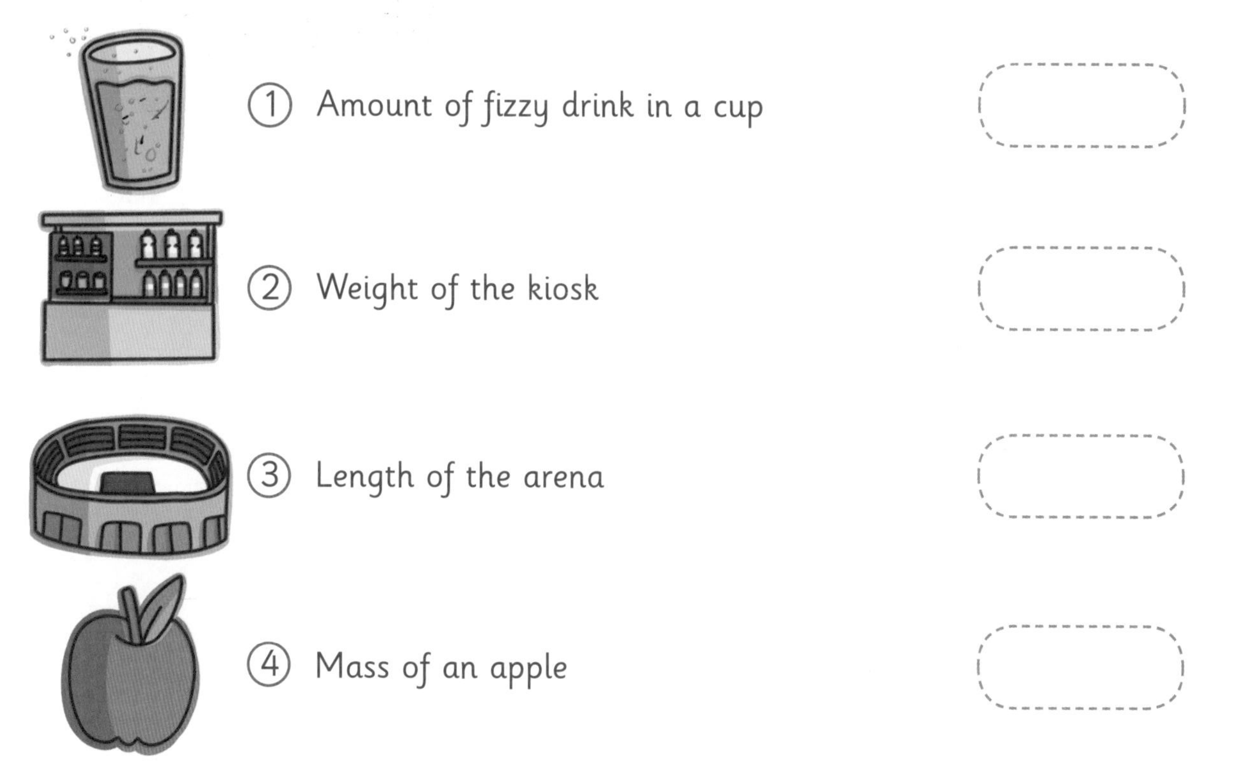

These are the weights of some of the refreshments. Put them in order from lightest to heaviest using the stickers on the sticker sheet.

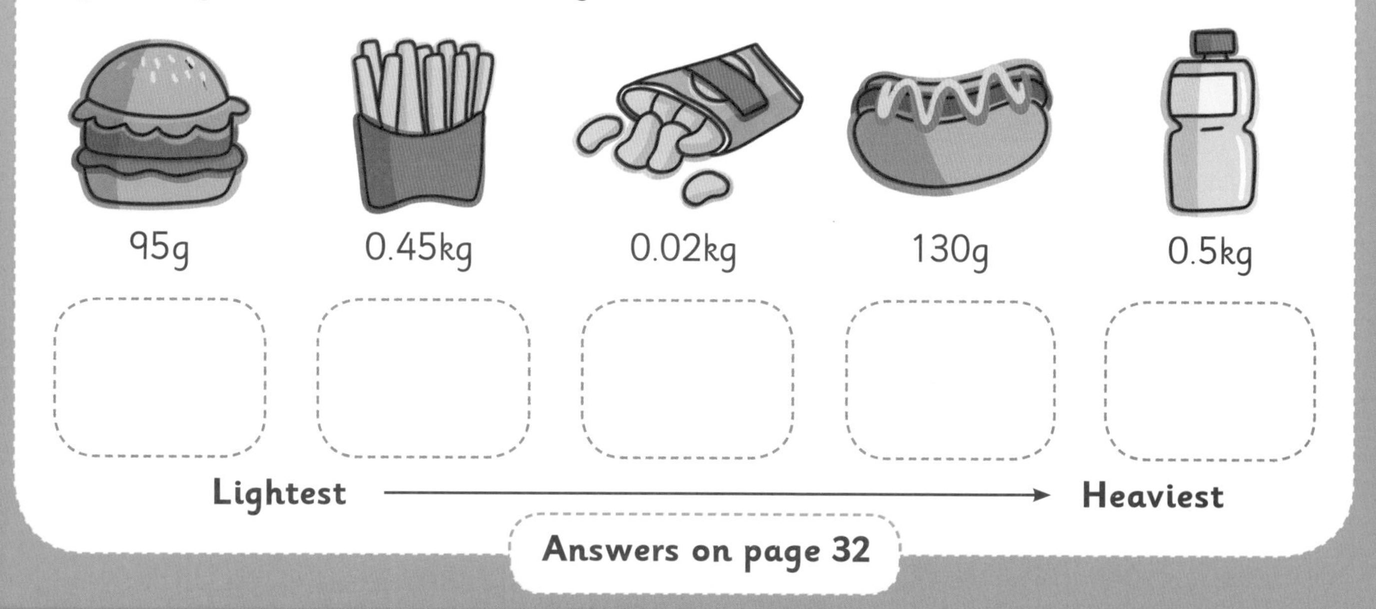

Answers on page 32

PARENT TIP: Give your child regular opportunities to familiarise themselves with measures in everyday life. While cooking, let them weigh ingredients and convert the measures to bigger or smaller units. When measuring to redecorate, let them use the tape measure and tell you the measurement in more than one way, for example 3.4m or 340cm.

Rounding whole numbers

Here is a table showing the number of fans for different teams watching a big football match on television. Round each of the first 3 teams' fans to complete the table.

Team	Fans	Nearest 1000	Nearest 10 000	Nearest 100 000
1	162 739			
2	250 182			
3	306 873			
4		224 000	220 000	200 000
5		178 000	180 000	200 000

(a) What could the number of fans be for the fourth team? Give 3 answers.

....

(b) Lily says that the smallest number of fans that team 5 could have is 178 001. Do you agree? Give a reason for your answer.

....

....

(c) When rounded to the nearest thousand, Team 6 rounds to 24 000 fans. Team 7 has 1 more fan and rounds to 25 000 fans. How many fans does each team have?

Team 6: .... Team 7: ....

Answers on page 32

Lucy and Rory are going to watch a football match live. They go online to work out how much money they will need to spend.

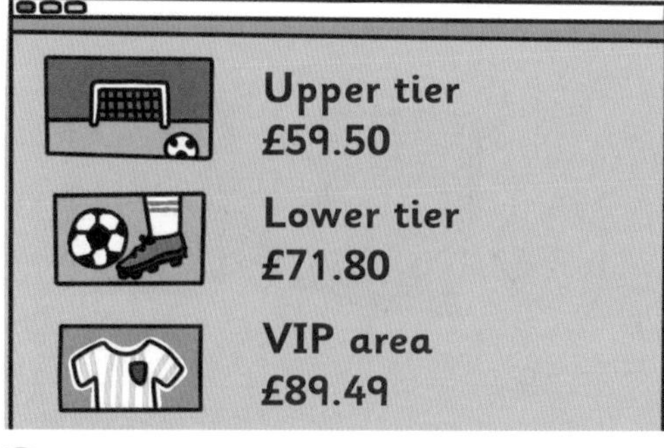

(d) Lucy chooses the ticket she wants and says it's about £72. Which ticket has she chosen?

....

(e) Rory wants to go to the VIP area. How much are these tickets to the nearest pound?

....

(f) They decide on VIP tickets. Lucy estimates the cost for two tickets as £180. Rory estimates it will be £178. How did they get different estimates?

....

(g) They look online to buy some merchandise for the match. Lucy says an away kit is about £20 but Rory says it is about £30. Who is correct and why?

....

....

(h) Lucy rounds the price of a hat to £23 to the nearest pound. What is the largest and smallest amount it might cost?

....

(i) Rory's dad tells him he can buy a souvenir with a price that rounds to £25. What can Rory buy?

....

Answers on page 32

PARENT TIP: Think of a number with up to 6 digits. For example, 371 348. Give your child clues, e.g. "My number rounds to 370 000 when rounded to the nearest 10 000. It rounds to 400 000 to the nearest 100 000. It rounds to 371 300 to the nearest 100". Can they guess your number? Try it for decimals using wholes, tenths and hundredths too.

Adding and subtracting mentally

Ben's mum and dad want to buy a few new electrical items. They ask Ben to work out the total costs of different combinations but he has no pen and paper so will need to do it mentally.

Can you use the stickers to show which strategy would be most efficient for each of the combinations?

£224 + £228

£532 + £1425

£416 + £532 + £224

£1425 + £199

(a) Ben likes a television that costs £2345 but mum and dad prefer one costing £1999. How much more does Ben's cost? Use jottings to show how you could do it mentally.

....

(b) Ben's parents have £3000 to spend. If they buy a television for £1400, a tablet for £350 and a games console costing £175, how much would they have left?

....

(c) They decide on a television costing £1465, a dvd player costing £270, a games console for £335 and two spare remotes each costing £15. What's the best order to add these prices? Show your jottings.

....

Answers on page 32

Adding and subtracting with written methods

The electrical store isn't making as much money now that online sales have increased, so Tim the manager is comparing the profits to the same time last year.

	Profit (£) last year	Profit (£) this year
January	239 962	182 045
February	161 528	94 387
March	97 037	87 238

Help Tim to work out the difference in profit for each of the first 3 months of the year.

January

```
  239 962
- 182 045
_________

_________
```

February

```
  161 528
-  94 387
_________

_________
```

March

```
  97 037
- 87 238
________

________
```

In which month were profits down the most? ....

Tim estimates that last year, the store made approximately £500 000 in the first 3 months, while this year it made only £360 000. How do you think he worked out these estimations?

....

Tim works out the total profit for the first 3 months of last year and compare it to this year. Complete his calculations for him.

```
  239 962
  161 528
+  97 037
_________

_________
```

```
  182 085
   94 387
+  87 238
_________

_________
```

Answers on page 32

PARENT TIP: Encourage your child to calculate mentally before using a written method wherever possible. Give them a set of numbers to choose from (e.g. 265, 198, 340, 980...). If they can solve it mentally, they get 3 points. If they solve it mentally with jottings, they get 2 points. If they use a written method, they get 1 point. Set a target for a reward.

Multiples

Tom and his friends are playing Laser Tag. Tom always aims for the shoulders so his score goes up in multiples of 3. Finlay shoots his opponents' backs so his score adds on 4 each time.

Which scores on the sticker sheet could have been seen on Tom and Finlay's packs during the game? Sort them into the Venn diagram.

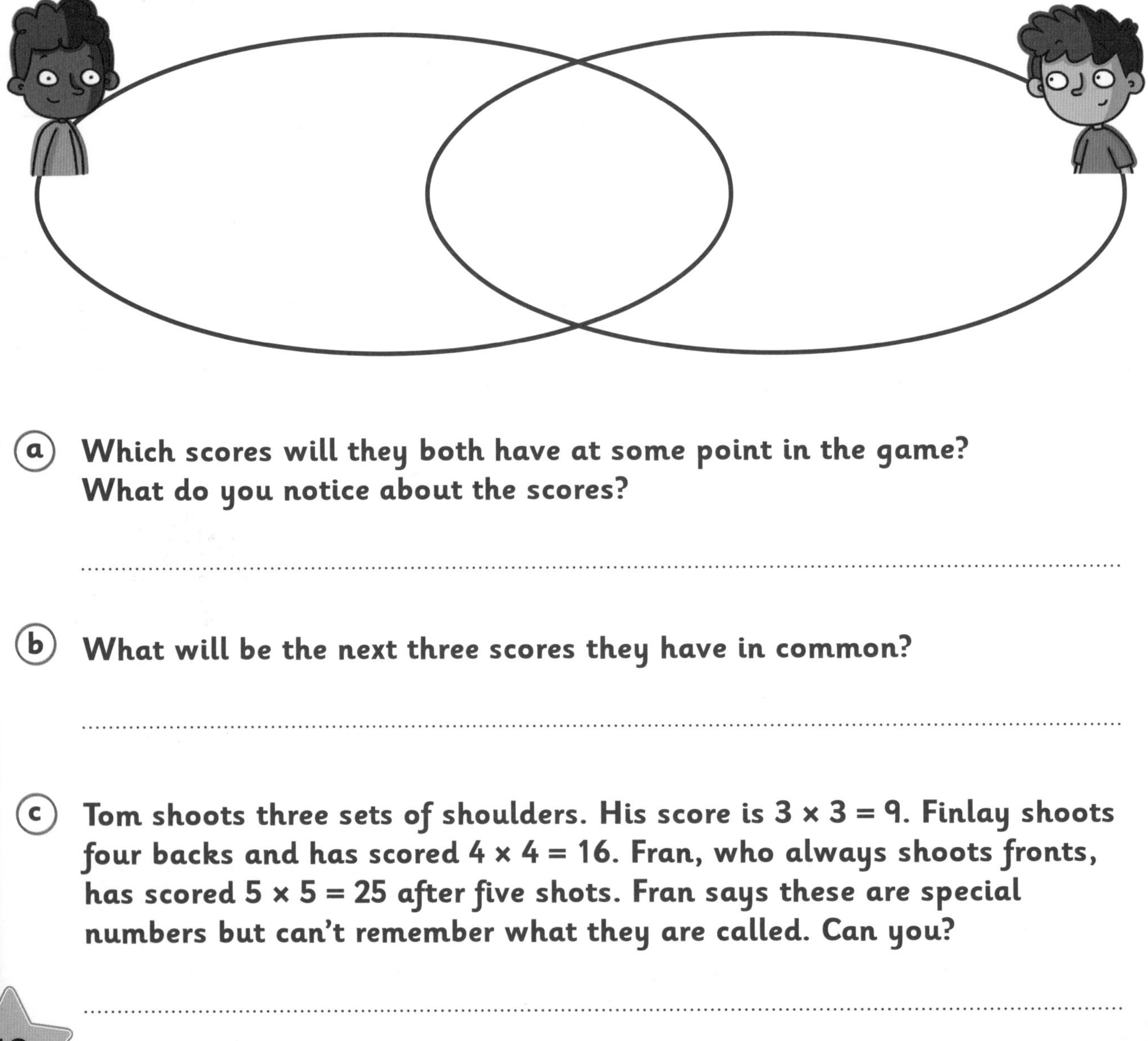

(a) Which scores will they both have at some point in the game? What do you notice about the scores?

....

(b) What will be the next three scores they have in common?

....

(c) Tom shoots three sets of shoulders. His score is $3 \times 3 = 9$. Finlay shoots four backs and has scored $4 \times 4 = 16$. Fran, who always shoots fronts, has scored $5 \times 5 = 25$ after five shots. Fran says these are special numbers but can't remember what they are called. Can you?

....

ⓓ **Give Fran three more examples of these numbers.**

....

ⓔ **Finlay says he knows some more special numbers called cube numbers. One is 2 × 2 × 2 = 8. Can you find the next three cube numbers?**

....

Later, they go for milkshakes and chat about the scoring system. They think there should be more ways to score points. They decide on new scores: Arms: 6 points, Upper legs: 7 points, Lower legs: 8 points, Hands: 9 points.

They play a game of *Guess our Target* using their new score system. The children each have a different target but fire the same number of shots. Can you guess the body parts each child is thinking of and work out how many shots they took?

....

ⓘ **Tom says that if they shoot more than one person, there are some scores that aren't possible like 3, 5 and 17. He thinks this is because they are odd numbers. Do you agree?**

....

ⓙ **Can you think of three more scores between 5 and 30 that aren't possible?**

....

Multiplying mentally

Poppy works at the cinema. She works on the refreshment kiosk on Friday night. The computer systems aren't working so she must work out all the costs mentally. Can you help her?

a) 85p × 4 = ... (use doubling to help you)

b) £3.50 × 14 = ... (double one and half the other)

c) £3.40 × 5 = ... (multiply by 10 and halve the answer)

On Saturday, Poppy is selling tickets. Children's tickets are £9 each and adults' are £13. For each question, circle your choice and find the total.

d) **8 adults pay for their tickets together. Poppy can't remember her 8 times table. How could she find the answer to £13 × 8?**

13 × 4 × 4   13 × 4 × 2   13 × 4 + 2

e) **23 children at a party buy tickets for a film. Poppy starts working out the total price by doing 23 × 10 but she isn't sure how to adjust the answer. What should she do?**

23 × 10 – 1   23 × 10 – 23   23 × 10 – 9

f) **12 seniors arrive. They pay £7 for their tickets. Holly doesn't know the answer to 7 × 12. Which of these calculations would not give her the answer? Can you explain why?**

12 × 5 + 12 × 2   10 × 7 + 2 × 7   11 × 7 + 11

....

Answers on page 32

The cinema has some special promotions on.

TICKET PRICES

ADULT: £13
CHILD: £9
FAMILY: £35
SENIOR: £7
COUPLE: £24

Poppy is curious about which types of tickets make the most money so she multiplies the number of each ticket sold this week by its price.

(g) £13 × 30 = ...

(h) £9 × 45 = ...

(i) £35 × 4 = ...

(j) £7 × 25 = ...

(k) £24 × 11 = ...

Which ticket type makes the most money?

....

The week after, Poppy does the same again but she makes some mistakes. Can you tell her what she has done wrong?

(l) £13 × 8 = 13 × 2 × 2 × 2 × 2 = £208

....

(m) £9 × 13 = 9 × 12 + 13 = £109

....

(n) £24 × 0 = £24

....

Answers on page 32

Dividing mentally

Martha works at the travel agents in the currency exchange. Today she is exchanging foreign currency back to British pounds for customers who didn't spend all the money they took on holiday.

These are the current exchange rates for different currencies per pound:

5 Turkish Lira	7 Ghanian Cedi
2 Australian Dollar	12 Swedish Krona
4 Brazilian Real	8 Croatian Kuna
6 Saudi Arabian Real	11 Hong Kong Dollars
9 Danish Krone	3 Barbadian Dollars

Martha knows she needs to divide the customers' amounts by the conversion rate (currency per pound). She is trying to use the best method for each conversion. Can you use her method to convert each amount?

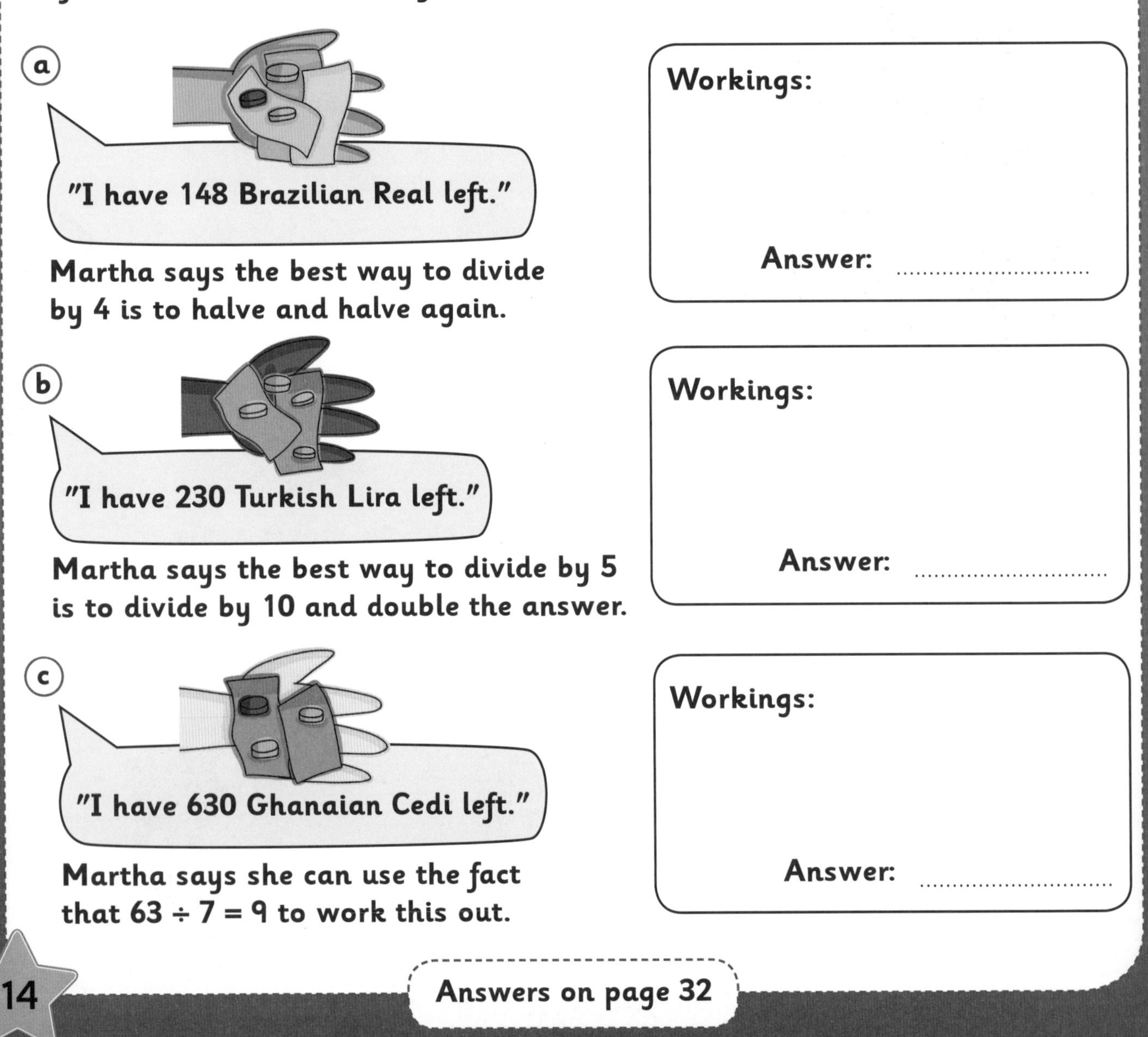

a "I have 148 Brazilian Real left."

Martha says the best way to divide by 4 is to halve and halve again.

Workings:

Answer: ....

b "I have 230 Turkish Lira left."

Martha says the best way to divide by 5 is to divide by 10 and double the answer.

Workings:

Answer: ....

c "I have 630 Ghanaian Cedi left."

Martha says she can use the fact that $63 \div 7 = 9$ to work this out.

Workings:

Answer: ....

Answers on page 32

Dividing with written methods

For these exchanges, Martha cannot find a good mental strategy so she uses a written method. Can you complete her calculations?

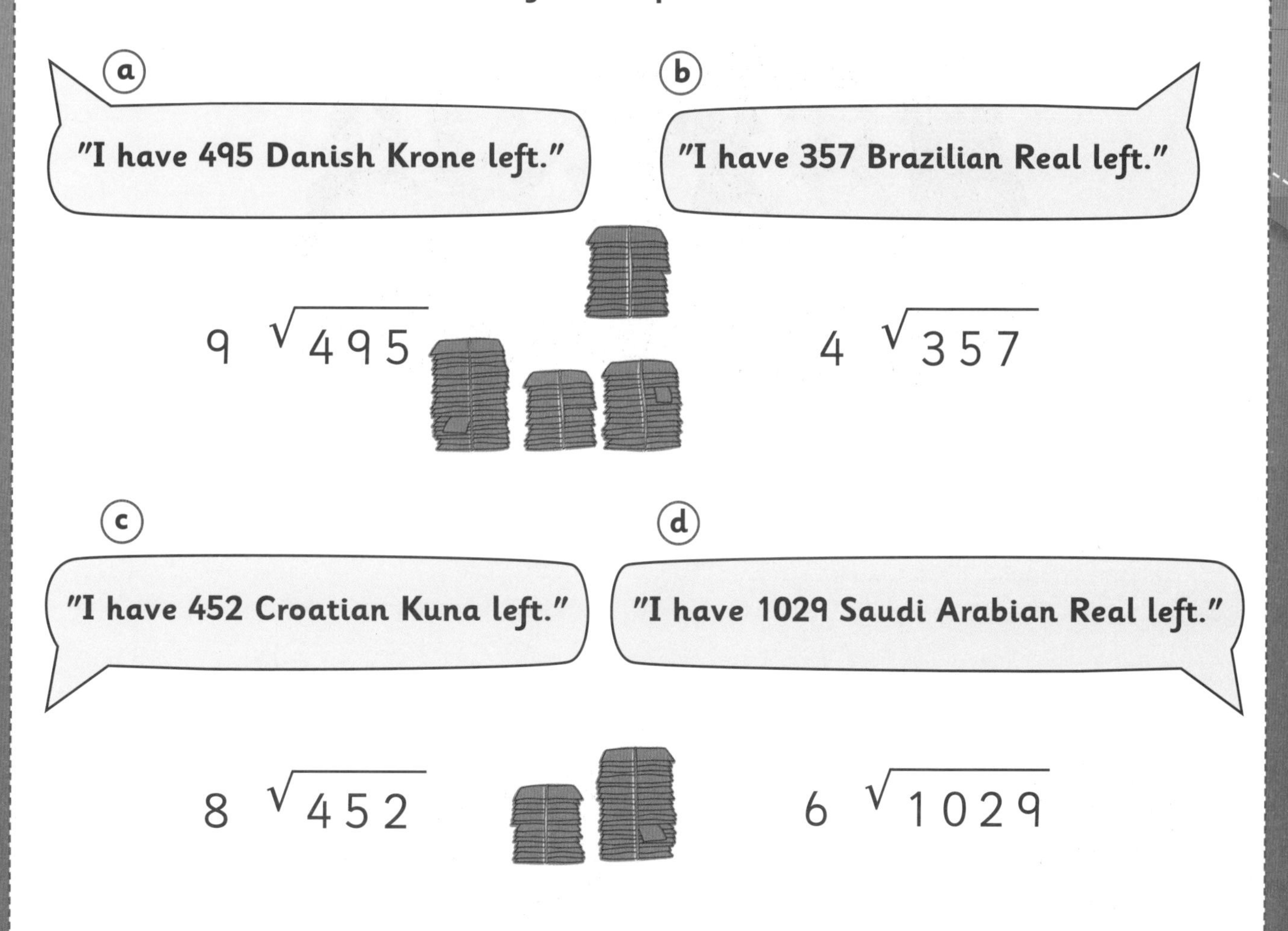

Martha's pen has leaked on these calculations. Can you work out what the missing digits might be? Use the stickers on the sticker sheet to cover over the pen splodges.

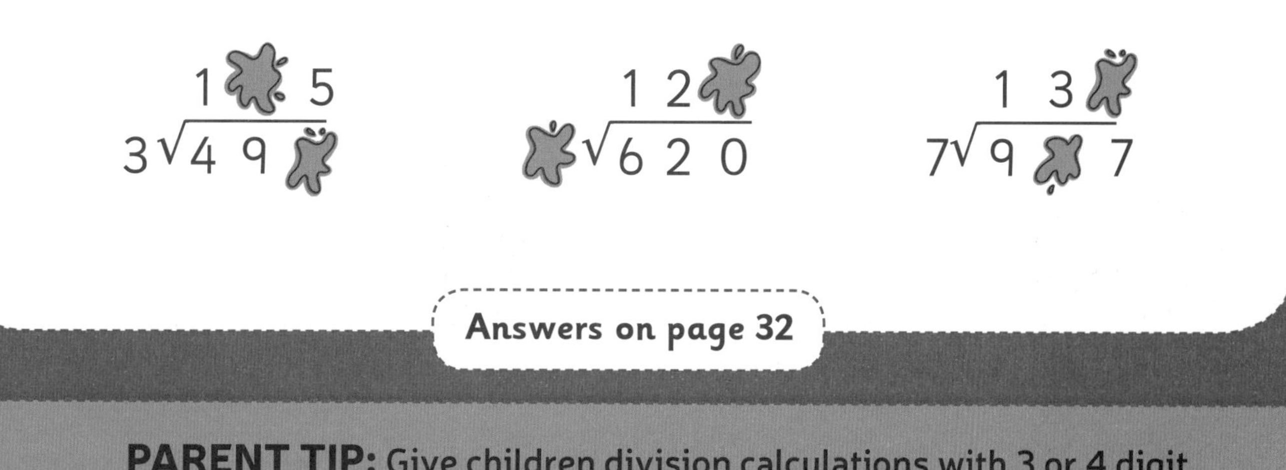

Answers on page 32

PARENT TIP: Give children division calculations with 3 or 4 digit numbers. Ask them to decide between a mental or written method. Encourage them to use a mental calculation first. Can they see any multiplication facts within the numbers? Can they use halving?

Ordering fractions

Lucy and her friends are having a sleepover at her house and all their parents have sent food for them to share.

Lucy has already eaten $\frac{1}{3}$ of her popcorn. Kirsty has eaten $\frac{2}{9}$ of hers. Who has eaten the most? Use equivalent fractions to prove it.

....

Compare these other amounts that each child has enjoyed by inserting the correct symbol from the sticker sheet.

a) $\frac{3}{4}$ ☐ $\frac{5}{8}$

b) $\frac{3}{5}$ ☐ $\frac{11}{15}$

c) $\frac{3}{4}$ ☐ $\frac{7}{10}$

d) $\frac{3}{4}$ ☐ $\frac{7}{12}$

Here are some more fractions separated by a symbol. Can you fill in the missing numerators and denominators?

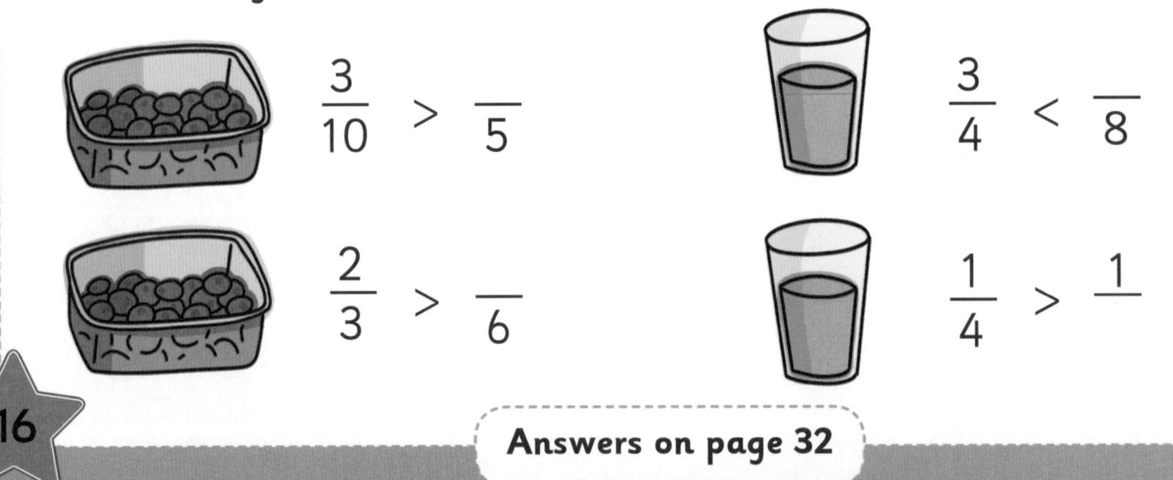

$\frac{3}{10} > \frac{\ }{5}$

$\frac{3}{4} < \frac{\ }{8}$

$\frac{2}{3} > \frac{\ }{6}$

$\frac{1}{4} > \frac{1}{\ }$

Answers on page 32

There are treats left over so the children combine them to keep for next time. Hannah and Francesca combine their snacks together. They have $1\frac{1}{4}$ boxes of popcorn. Hannah says this is $\frac{5}{4}$ because there are 4 quarters in a whole box plus the quarter left over. Can you convert their other amounts into improper fractions?

$2\frac{1}{3} = \frac{\quad}{3}$

$5\frac{1}{2} = \frac{\quad}{2}$

$1\frac{5}{8} = \frac{\quad}{8}$

$3\frac{3}{4} = \frac{\quad}{4}$

Lucy combines her leftovers with Alice and Jasmine. Kirsty combines hers with Sophie and Amira. Which group has the most left over? Insert the correct symbol from the sticker sheet.

(a) Lucy's group $2\frac{1}{4}$ ☐ Kirsty's group $\frac{7}{4}$

(b) Lucy's group $2\frac{1}{5}$ ☐ Kirsty's group $\frac{12}{5}$

(c) Lucy's group $\frac{11}{8}$ ☐ Kirsty's group $1\frac{5}{8}$

(d) Lucy's group $2\frac{14}{3}$ ☐ Kirsty's group $5\frac{1}{3}$

The two groups combine their leftover pizza and ice cream. How much do they have in total?

$2\frac{1}{4} + \frac{7}{4} =$

$2\frac{1}{5} + \frac{12}{5} =$

Answers on page 32

PARENT TIP: Cut up food into equal parts so your child can see how the parts relate to each other, e.g. a cake cut into thirds has half as many pieces as a cake cut into sixths. Can they compare $\frac{2}{3}$ to $\frac{5}{6}$, using equivalent fractions to change thirds into sixths? Then they can add $\frac{2}{3}$ of one cake to $\frac{5}{6}$ of another and work out how much they have in total.

Adding and subtracting fractions

Sean and Robin have been washing the neighbours' cars over the summer holidays. At the end of each day, they measure how much detergent they each have left in their bottles. Can you use equivalent fractions to work out how much they have left in total? The first one has been done for you.

	Sean	Robin	Total
Monday	$\frac{1}{5}$	$\frac{7}{10}$	$\frac{1}{5} + \frac{7}{10} = \frac{2}{10} + \frac{7}{10} = \frac{9}{10}$
Tuesday	$\frac{3}{4}$	$\frac{3}{12}$	
Wednesday	$\frac{1}{2}$	$\frac{2}{5}$	
Thursday	$\frac{2}{3}$	$\frac{1}{5}$	
Friday	$\frac{1}{6}$	$\frac{3}{8}$	

The following week, they use up some of the leftovers. They subtract how much they used each day from how much was in the bottle at the start of the day, then cancel the fraction to its simplest form. How much do they have left each day? The first one has been done for you.

	Amount at start of day	Amount at end of day	Total
Monday	$\frac{3}{4}$	$\frac{5}{8}$	$\frac{3}{4} - \frac{5}{8} = \frac{6}{8} - \frac{5}{8} = \frac{1}{8}$
Tuesday	$1\frac{1}{5}$	$\frac{7}{10}$	
Wednesday	$1\frac{1}{3}$	$\frac{5}{12}$	
Thursday	$1\frac{1}{6}$	$\frac{3}{4}$	
Friday	$1\frac{2}{3}$	$\frac{3}{5}$	

Answers on page 32

At the end of the summer, they have a lot of bottles with different amounts of detergent left inside. They sort them into piles of the same fraction. Can you use these diagrams to help you work out how much is left altogether? Show your workings.

Answers on page 32

PARENT TIP: Give children real objects that can be broken into fractions and ask them to multiply them by a whole number. Repeatedly add the same amount. Only the numerator (top part of the fraction) is multiplied (e.g. $\frac{2}{3}$ of a cake x 4 = $\frac{8}{3}$ or $2\frac{2}{3}$).

Percentages

Sadie and her two friends all have tablets but they notice their battery indicators show the power remaining in different ways. Ethan's red tablet shows a fraction. Vicki's blue tablet shows a decimal. Sadie's yellow tablet shows a percentage.

Using the stickers on the sticker sheet, put their tablets into groups where they all show the same battery power. One group has been done for you.

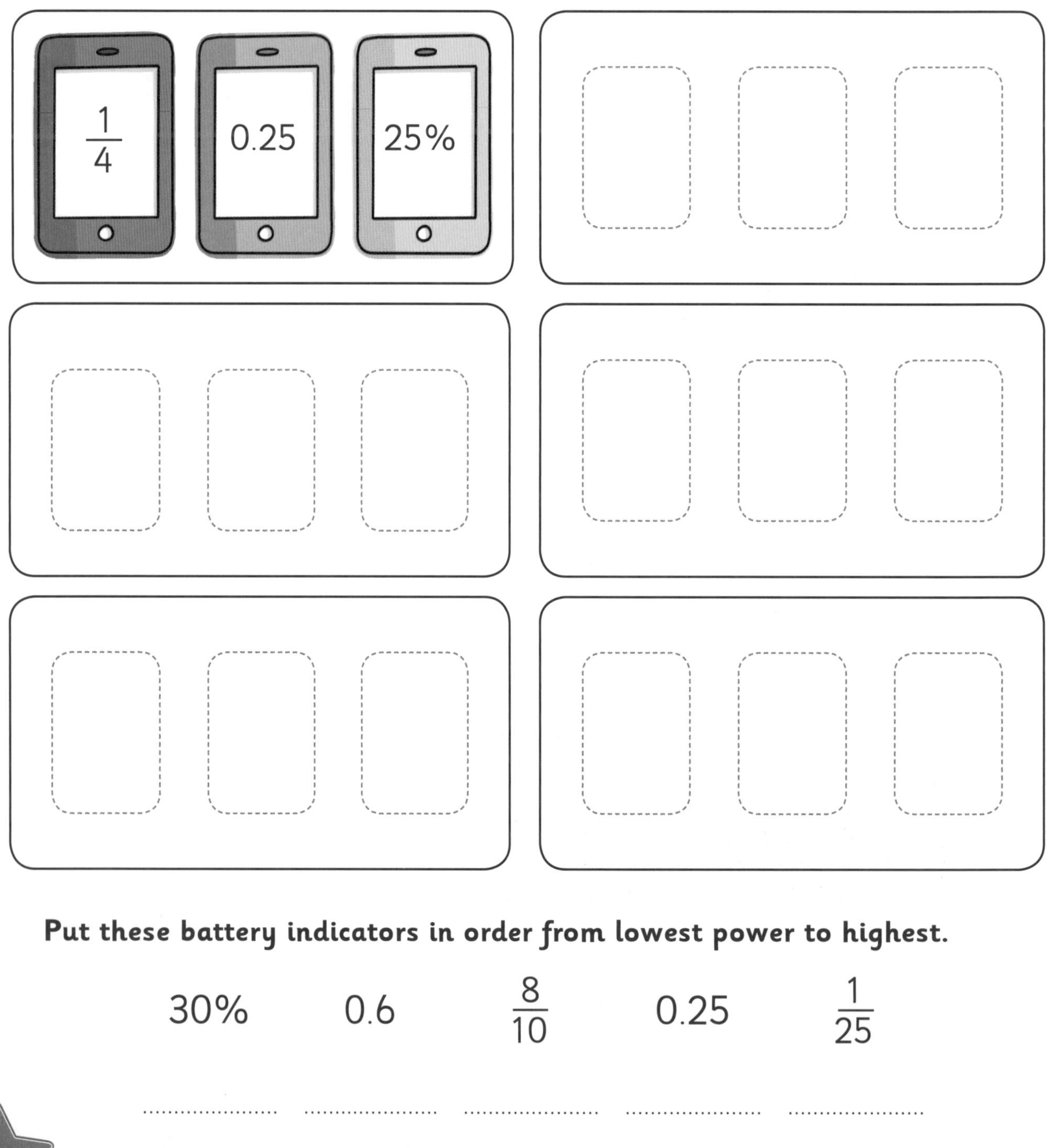

Put these battery indicators in order from lowest power to highest.

30%   0.6 $\frac{8}{10}$ 0.25 $\frac{1}{25}$

....

Answers on page 32

(a) Ethan has used $\frac{7}{10}$ of his battery power. What percentage has he got left?

....

(b) Vicki's tablet shows 0.2 remaining. What fraction would Ethan's show? Write the fraction in its simplest form.

....

(c) Sadie's tablet shows 60% remaining. How much power has she used? Give the answer as a decimal.

....

(d) Ethan has $\frac{3}{10}$ left. Sadie has 35%. Who has the most and by how much?

....

....

(e) Vicki has 0.45 left and Sadie has 30%. How much more has Vicki got? Give the answer as a fraction in its simplest form.

....

....

(f) Ethan has $\frac{2}{5}$ left. Sadie has 10% more. What does her display show?

....

Answers on page 32

PARENT TIP: Play 'percentage patience'. Write these fractions, percentages and decimals on small pieces of card: 0.5, 50%, $\frac{3}{10}$, 0.3, $\frac{1}{4}$, 0.25, $\frac{7}{10}$, 70%, 40%, 4%, $\frac{3}{5}$, 0.6. Place them upside down spread over a table. Take turns with your child to turn them over, 2 at a time. The aim is to find a matching pair. When you do, keep both cards. If they don't match, turn them upside down again.

Shapes

Karl has been learning about shapes at school but struggles to remember all their properties. He has downloaded an app to help him. He has to decide if the shape is regular or irregular. Can you help him? Use the regular and irregular polygons on your sticker sheet and place them in the correct side of the table below.

Regular polygons	Irregular polygons

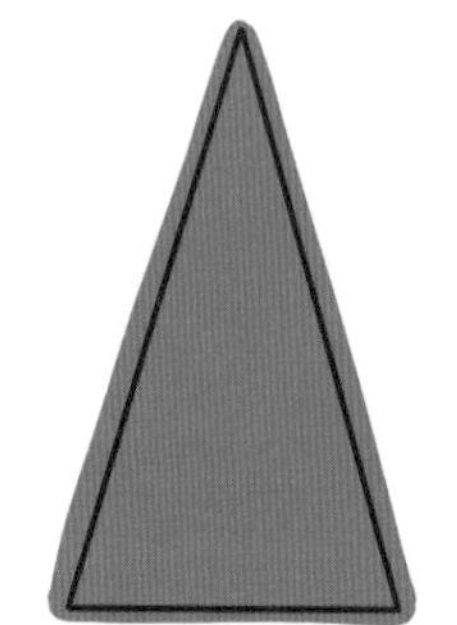

(a) Karl thinks this triangle is regular because it has two equal sides. Do you agree? Explain why.

....

....

(b) Karl thinks this rectangle is regular because it has equal angles. Do you agree? Explain why.

....

....

(c) Can you give Karl two rules to check any polygon is regular?

....

....

Answers on page 32

Karl's app asks him to identify 3D shapes from their properties. Use the properties to work out the name of the shape from the list below, then fill in the vertices and edges. Finally, add a sticker of the shape.
Shape names: hexagonal prism, triangular prism, cuboid, square-based pyramid, triangular-based pyramid, cylinder.

6 rectangular faces
2 hexagonal faces

☐ vertices
☐ edges

1 square face
4 triangular faces

☐ vertices
☐ edges

3 rectangular faces
2 triangular faces

☐ vertices
☐ edges

2 circular faces
1 curved face

☐ vertices
☐ edges

6 rectangular faces
3 pairs of equal faces

☐ vertices
☐ edges

4 triangular faces

☐ vertices
☐ edges

Answers on page 32

PARENT TIP: Ask your child to identify shapes around them (2D and 3D). Where do we see prisms? For example, on food packaging – go to the supermarket and see how many prism-shaped boxes you can find. Why is a cuboid such a useful shape?

Angles

On their residential trip, the children from Year 5 are orienteering. The teacher starts the groups off two at a time from the side of the building and they head off in two different directions. Complete the missing angle in each diagram.

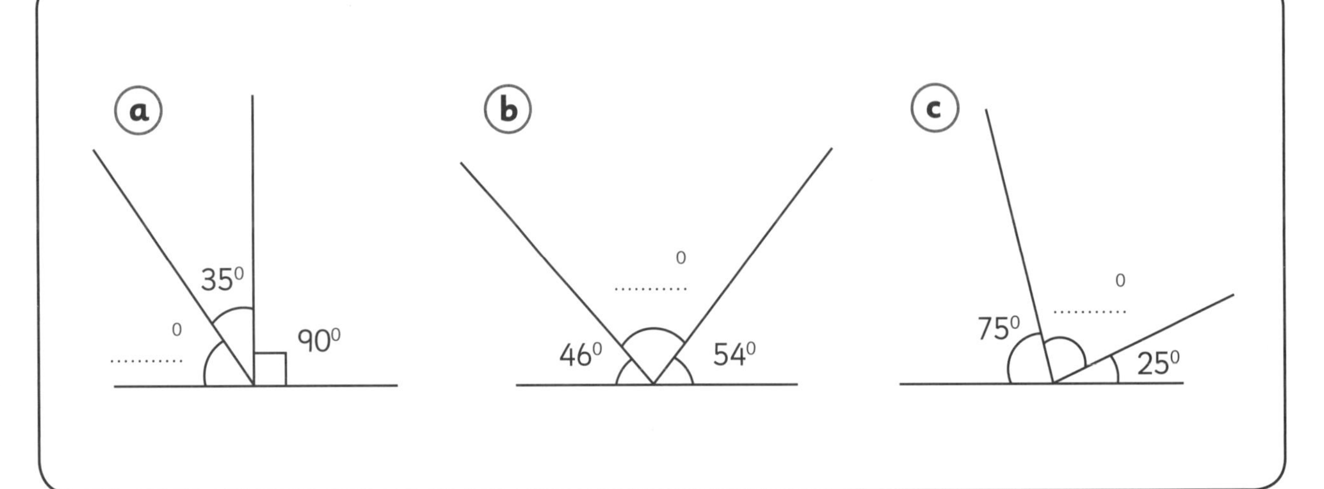

Jess and Natalie finish early so they play a game. Their teacher calls out instructions at random. The first to face the start again wins. Here are the instructions they each follow, turning clockwise each time:

Jess	Natalie
quarter turn	half turn
half turn	three quarter turn
2 half turns	half turn
three quarter turn	one and a half turns
quarter turn	quarter turn
one and a half turns	one and a half turns
three quarter turn	quarter turn

Who will face the start again first?

....

The children in Ali's group always seem to disagree on which direction they should walk. Mark the missing angles on each diagram to show the angle that Ali, Ben and Chris each turn from one another.

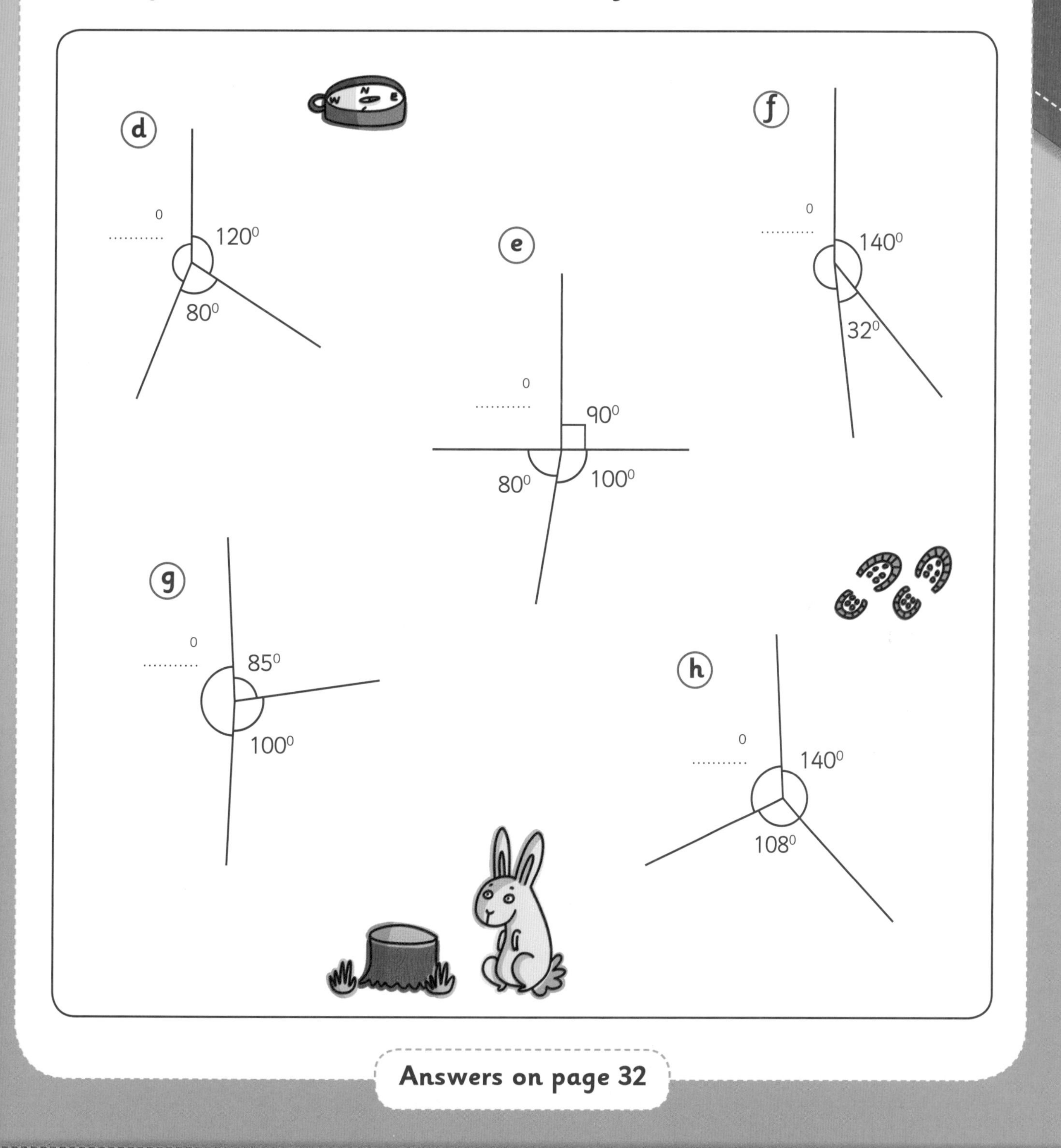

Answers on page 32

PARENT TIP: Play games that involve turning to quarter, half, three quarter and full turns, like Jess and Natalie's. Write instructions on cards to take from a pile at random. To make it more interesting, add the words 'clockwise' and 'anti-clockwise' to the instructions.

Imperial measures

Liam and his grandma decide to bake a cake together. Grandma's recipe gives measurements in imperial units but her new weighing scales are in metric units. She knows that 1 pound (lb) is 16 ounces (oz) and 1 ounce (oz) is about the same as 30 grams (g).

These are all the ingredients they need to weigh. Complete the table showing the metric measures they should use.

	Imperial	Metric
Butter	1 lb	
Self-raising flour	8 oz	
Caster sugar	6 oz	
Raisins	4 oz	
Cherries	2 oz	

They also need some liquid ingredients. Grandma knows that 1 pint is 568ml. They need half a pint of milk. How many ml is this? Explain how you know.

....

....

Liam estimates that a pint is just over half a litre. Using his estimation, can you compare each pair of measurements by adding one of these symbols: < > =

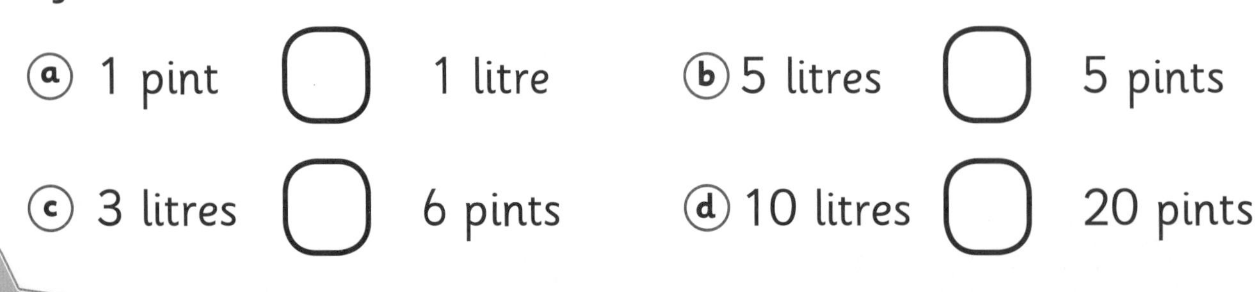

(e) **Liam helps Grandma make a pie. They need to roll out some pastry. Grandma tells Liam he needs to roll out half a foot of pastry for the base and 4 inches for the lid, but his ruler only has metric measures marked. She tells him that 1 foot = 30cm and 1 inch = 2.5cm.**

How many cm should he measure? ....

Grandma gives Liam some more measurements to practise converting. Can you help Liam by matching these imperial and metric measurements?

3 feet	10cm
4 inches	0.45m
$1\frac{1}{2}$ feet	90cm

Over dinner, Grandma checks what Liam has learnt by playing 'Would you rather...?' Assuming Liam likes each thing, what do you think he answered to each question?

(f) 1 pint of hot chocolate or 1 litre of hot chocolate? ....

(g) 3 inches of chocolate or 3cm of chocolate? ....

(h) 1 foot of pound coins in a line or 1m of pound coins in a line? ....

(i) 20 ounces of sweets or 20g of sweets? ....

(j) 1 pound of strawberries or 1 kilogram of strawberries? ....

Answers on page 32

PARENT TIP: Give children lots of opportunities in everyday life to use metric and imperial measurements. Encourage your child to do the weighing when you are baking and use recipes that have both units. Look at tape measures and use both sides to play games. For example, ask how many cm are in 6 inches, then turn the tape to see if they were right!

Perimeter and area

Sasha loves ice skating and has visited lots of different ice rinks. She likes to have lots of space to move around. Which of these is the biggest? Find their areas and write it on the dotted lines, then write numbers in the circle next to each one to show which is the biggest from 1 to 5.

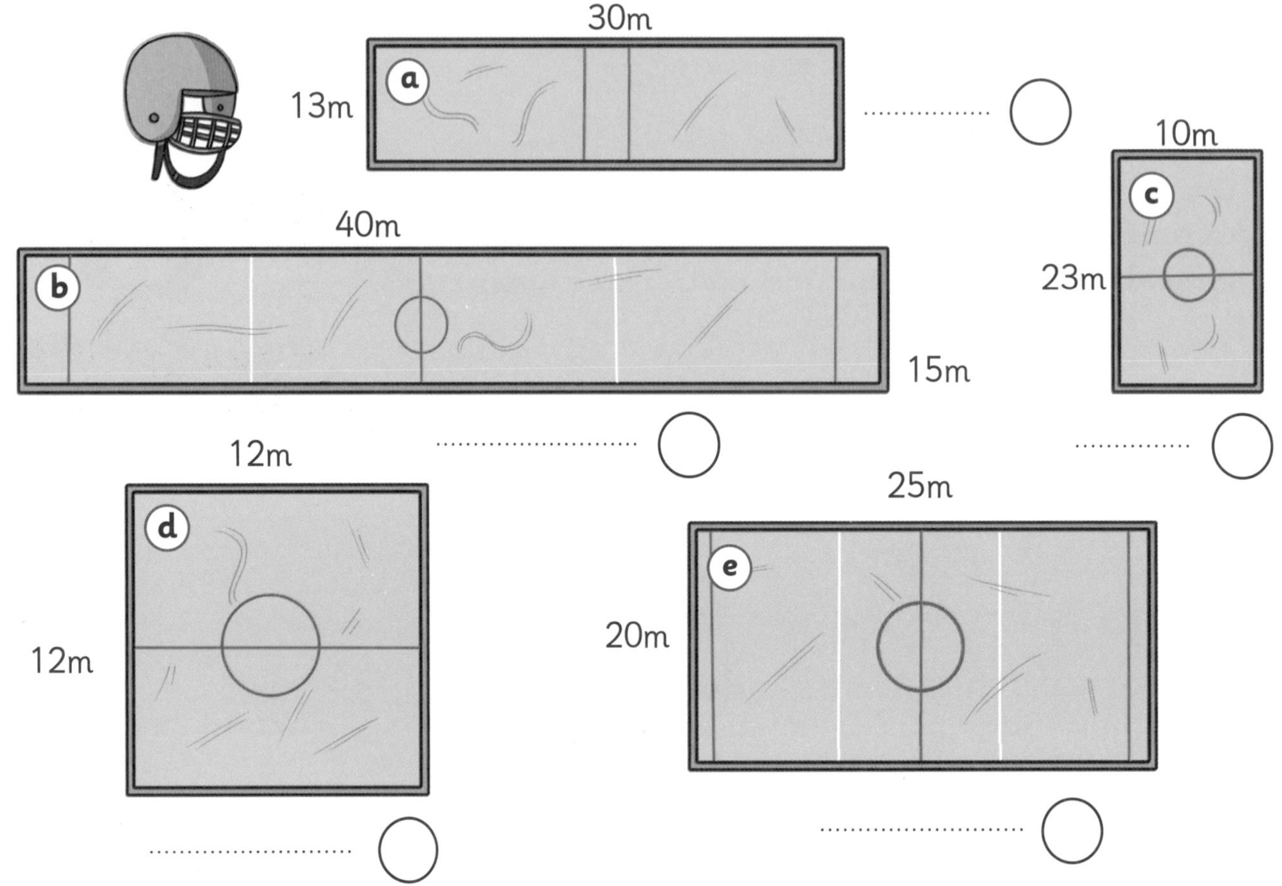

In the winter, she often goes to outdoor ice rinks like this one.
Can you estimate its area by counting the squares on the square grid?
(Count any square greater than half as a whole and any less than half as 0). Write the area on the dotted line below.

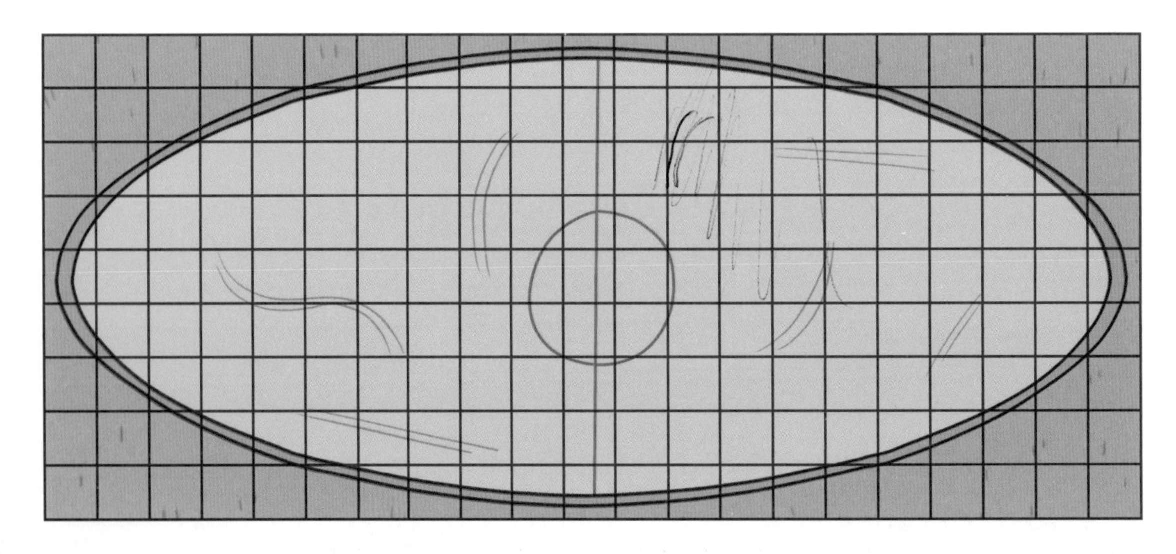

....

At Sasha's favourite ice rink, they are repainting the walls. The buildings are all different shapes. Can you work out the perimeter of each building so the decorators can work out how much paint they need? The manager has forgotten to measure some walls but can you work out the missing measures?

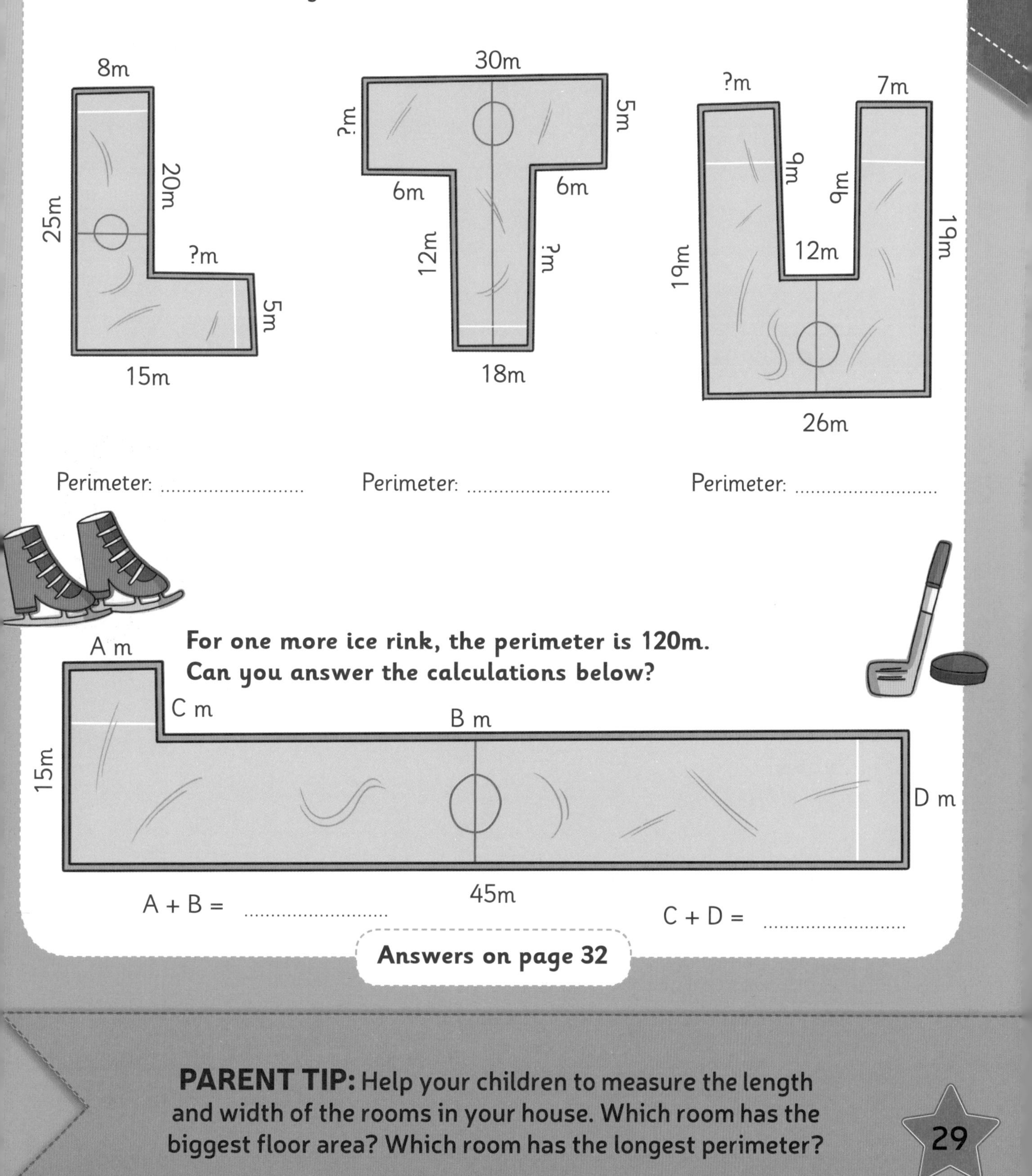

For one more ice rink, the perimeter is 120m. Can you answer the calculations below?

Answers on page 32

PARENT TIP: Help your children to measure the length and width of the rooms in your house. Which room has the biggest floor area? Which room has the longest perimeter?

Line graphs

Jay was given a drone for his birthday and went straight outside to test it out. The drone records its height above ground every minute, which you can see in this line graph.

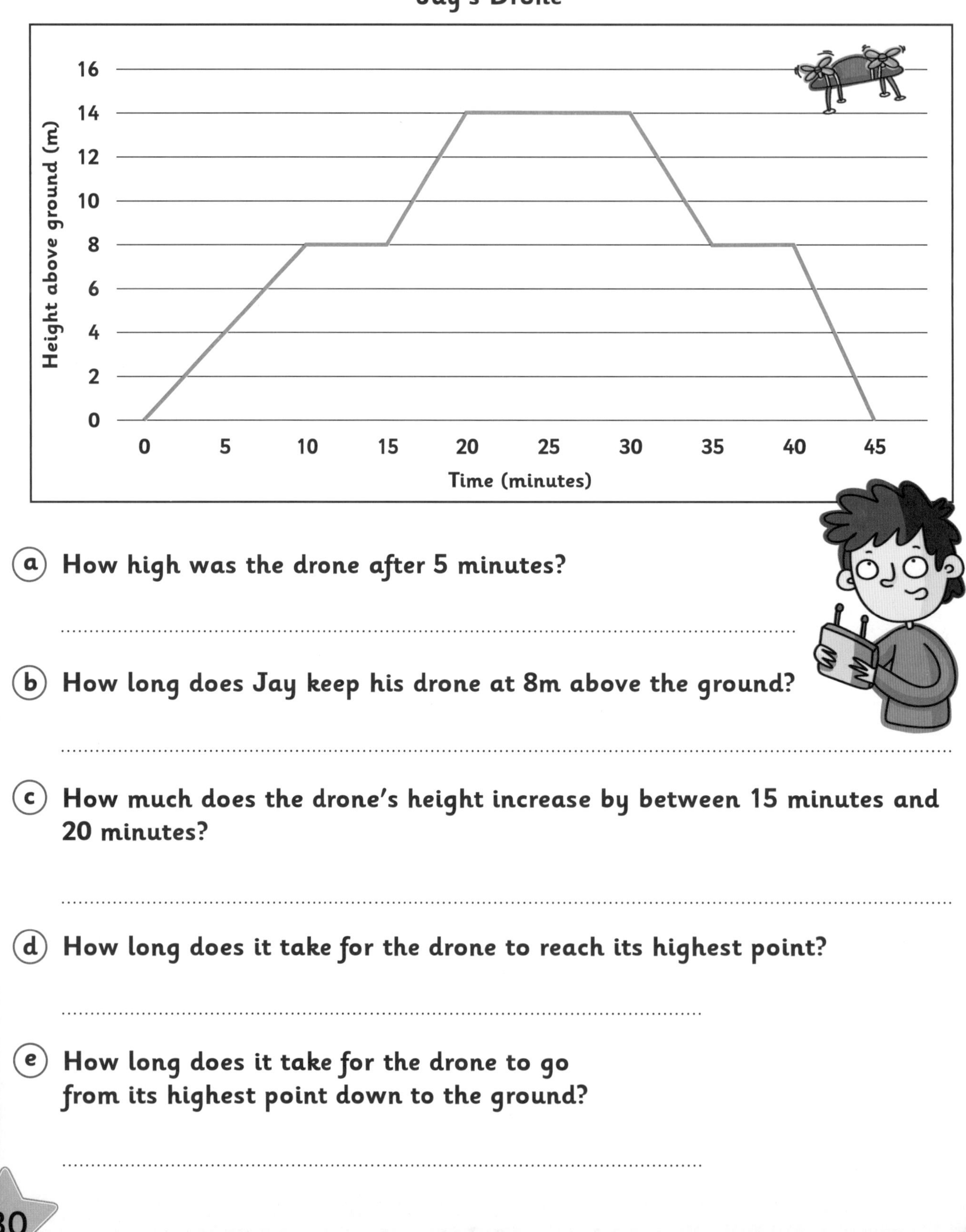

ⓐ How high was the drone after 5 minutes?

....

ⓑ How long does Jay keep his drone at 8m above the ground?

....

ⓒ How much does the drone's height increase by between 15 minutes and 20 minutes?

....

ⓓ How long does it take for the drone to reach its highest point?

....

ⓔ How long does it take for the drone to go from its highest point down to the ground?

....

Jay's friend, Martha, has come around with her drone and the two of them compete to see who can keep their drone in the air for the longest time.

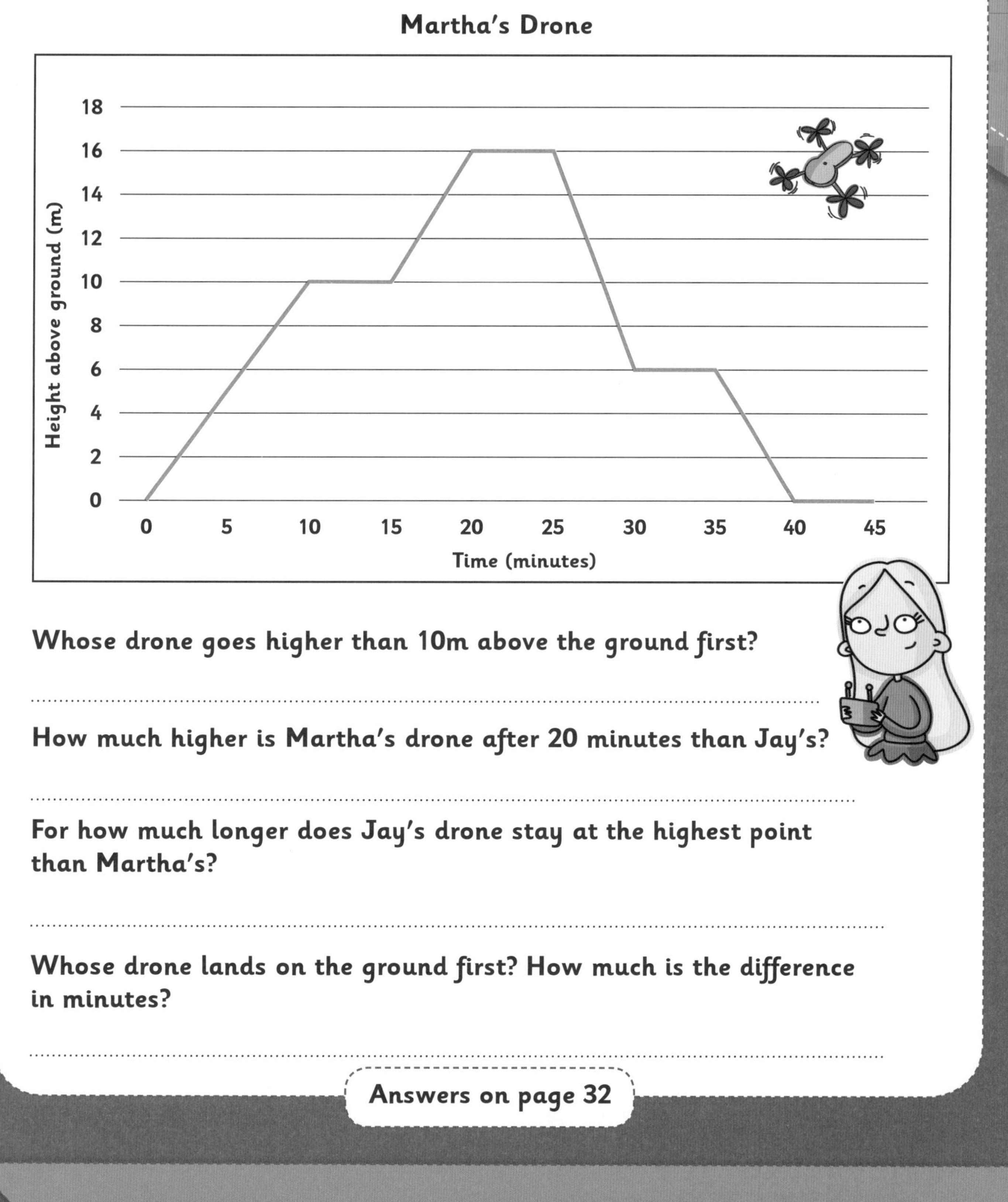

Whose drone goes higher than 10m above the ground first?

....

How much higher is Martha's drone after 20 minutes than Jay's?

....

For how much longer does Jay's drone stay at the highest point than Martha's?

....

Whose drone lands on the ground first? How much is the difference in minutes?

....

Answers on page 32

PARENT TIP: Encourage your child to draw their own graphs by collecting data from the things they do every day. This type of graph is suitable for measurements that change over time, such as the height of a plant growing in the garden or the distance travelled on a long journey.

Answers

Page 2: Big numbers

1. two hundred and sixty thousand seven hundred and forty-five pounds.
2. two hundred and twenty-five thousand nine hundred and eighty-five pounds
3. two hundred and nine thousand four hundred and fifty-nine pounds
4. two hundred and twenty-nine thousand nine hundred and ninety-five pounds.

Correct order: £209 459 (house 3), £225 985 (house 2), £229 995 (house 4), £260 745 (house 1).

Reduced by: 1. £16 000 2. £8 000 3. £20 000 4. £2 000.

Page 3: Decimal numbers

House 2 has 5 tenths but the others have less than 5 tenths so are all smaller.

House 1 is closest to Jamie's friend's house.

Pages 4–5: Multiplying and dividing by 10, 100 and 1000

There were 23 000 fans altogether. 342 x 10 = 3420

7.5 x 1000 = 7500   100 x 24 = 2400   100 x 30 = 3000

	x1	x10	x100	x1000
Fizzy drinks	£1.99	£19.90	£199	£1990
Portion of chips	£2.30	£23	£230	£2300
Burgers	£3.50	£35	£350	£3500
Popcorn	£2.05	£20.50	£205	£2050
Chocolate bars	£0.95	£9.50	£95	£950

1. millilitres 2. tonnes 3. metres 4. grams

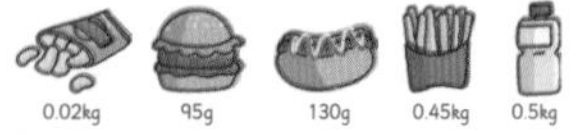

Pages 6–7: Rounding whole numbers

Team	Fans	Nearest 1000	Nearest 10 000	Nearest 100 000
1	162 739	163 000	160 000	200 000
2	250 182	250 000	250 000	300 000
3	306 873	307 000	310 000	300 000

a. Answers are any three numbers between 223 500–224 499 inclusive.
b. No, because any number above 177 500 rounds up to 178 000.
c. Team 6: 24 499, Team 7: 24 500. **d.** Lower tier. **e.** £89 **f.** Lucy rounded to the nearest £10 and Rory to the nearest £1. **g.** Lucy is correct: the 4 of the £24 rounds down to £20, not up to £30. **h.** Smallest: £22.50, largest: £23.49. **i.** Away kit OR home kit (both answers are correct).

Page 8: Adding and subtracting mentally

£224 + £228: near doubles.   £416 + £532 + £224: reordering.
£532 + £1425: partitioning.   £1425 + £199: rounding and adjusting.
a. 2345 – 1999 = 2345 – 2000 + 1 = 346. **b.** £1075.
c. 1465 + 335 (makes 1800) and 270 + 15 + 15 (makes 300), then 1800 + 300 (makes 2100).

Page 9: Adding and subtracting with written methods

January	February	March
239 962	161 528	97 037
–182 045	– 94 387	– 87 238
57 917	67 141	9 799

Profits were most down in February. Tim rounded to the nearest ten thousand. (Last year: 240 000 + 160 000 + 100 000 = 500 000. This year: 180 000 + 90 000 + 90 000 = 360 000).

239 962	182 085
161 528	94 387
+ 97 037	+ 87 238
498 527	363 710

Pages 10–11: Multiples

Tom: 18, 42, 9, 21 | Tom and Finlay: 12, 36, 48, 24 | Finlay: 8, 32, 44, 20

a. 12, 24, 36, 48. These are multiples of 12. **b.** 60, 72, 84.
c. Square numbers. **d.** Example answers: 4, 36, 49, 64, 81, 100. **e.** 3 x 3 x 3 = 27, 4 x 4 x 4 = 64, 5 x 5 x 5 = 125.
f. Tom: upper legs, Fran: lower legs, 7 shots. **g.** Fran: upper legs, Finley: hands, 12 shots. **h.** Finlay: arms, Tom: hands, 8 shots. **i.** No, it is because they are prime numbers. **j.** Any three answers from 7, 11, 13, 19, 23, 29.

Pages 12–13: Multiplying mentally

a. £3.40 **b.** £49 **c.** £17 **d.** 13 x 4 x 2 **e.** 23 x 10 – 23 **f.** 11 x 7 + 11 (she should add 7, not 11). **g.** £390 **h.** £405 **i.** £140 **j.** £175 **k.** £264. Children's tickets make the most money. **l.** Poppy doubled four times. She should have doubled three times. **m.** She should have added 9, not 13.
n. Multiplying any number by 0 = 0.

Page 14: Dividing mentally

a. 148 ÷ 2 ÷ 2 = £37 **b.** 230 ÷ 10 x 2 = £46 **c.** 630 ÷ 7 = £90

Page 15: Dividing with written methods

a. £55 **b.** £89.25 **c.** £56.50 **d.** £171.50

$3\overline{)495} = 165$ $5\overline{)620} = 124$ $7\overline{)917} = 131$

Pages 16–17: Ordering fractions

Lucy $\frac{1}{3} = \frac{3}{9}$ **a.** > **b.** < **c.** > **d.** >

$\frac{3}{10} > \frac{1}{5}$ $\frac{3}{4} < \frac{8}{8}$ or $\frac{7}{8}$ $\frac{2}{3} > \frac{1}{6}$ or $\frac{2}{6}$ or $\frac{3}{6}$ $\frac{1}{4} > \frac{1}{*}$

*This denominator can be any digit greater than 4.

$2\frac{1}{3} = \frac{7}{3}$ $5\frac{1}{2} = \frac{11}{2}$ $1\frac{5}{8} = \frac{13}{8}$ $3\frac{3}{4} = \frac{15}{4}$

a. > **b.** < **c.** < **d.** >

$2\frac{1}{4} + \frac{7}{4} = \frac{9}{4} + \frac{7}{4} = \frac{16}{4} = \frac{4}{1} = 4$ pizzas

$2\frac{1}{5} + \frac{12}{5} = \frac{11}{5} + \frac{12}{5} = \frac{23}{5} = 4\frac{3}{5}$ ice creams

Pages 18–19: Adding and subtracting fractions

	Sean	Robin	Total
Monday	$\frac{1}{5}$	$\frac{7}{10}$	$\frac{1}{5} + \frac{7}{10} = \frac{2}{10} + \frac{7}{10} = \frac{9}{10}$
Tuesday	$\frac{3}{4}$	$\frac{3}{12}$	$\frac{3}{4} + \frac{3}{12} = \frac{9}{12} + \frac{3}{12} = \frac{12}{12} = 1$
Wednesday	$\frac{1}{2}$	$\frac{2}{5}$	$\frac{1}{2} + \frac{2}{5} = \frac{5}{10} + \frac{4}{10} = \frac{9}{10}$
Thursday	$\frac{2}{3}$	$\frac{1}{5}$	$\frac{2}{3} + \frac{1}{5} = \frac{10}{15} + \frac{3}{15} = \frac{13}{15}$
Friday	$\frac{1}{6}$	$\frac{3}{8}$	$\frac{1}{6} + \frac{3}{8} = \frac{4}{24} + \frac{9}{24} = \frac{13}{24}$

	Amount at start of day	Amount at end of day	Total
Monday	$\frac{3}{4}$	$\frac{5}{8}$	$\frac{3}{4} - \frac{5}{8} = \frac{6}{8} - \frac{5}{8} = \frac{1}{8}$
Tuesday	$1\frac{1}{5}$	$\frac{7}{10}$	$\frac{6}{5} - \frac{7}{10} = \frac{12}{10} - \frac{7}{10} = \frac{5}{10} = \frac{1}{2}$
Wednesday	$1\frac{1}{3}$	$\frac{5}{12}$	$\frac{4}{3} - \frac{5}{12} = \frac{16}{12} - \frac{5}{12} = \frac{11}{12}$
Thursday	$1\frac{1}{6}$	$\frac{3}{4}$	$\frac{7}{6} - \frac{3}{4} = \frac{28}{24} - \frac{18}{24} = \frac{10}{24} = \frac{5}{12}$
Friday	$1\frac{2}{3}$	$\frac{3}{5}$	$\frac{5}{3} - \frac{3}{5} = \frac{25}{15} - \frac{9}{15} = \frac{16}{15}$

a. $\frac{2}{3} \times 3 = \frac{6}{3} = 2$ **b.** $\frac{3}{4} \times 5 = \frac{15}{4} = 3\frac{3}{4}$ **c.** $\frac{2}{5} \times 4 = \frac{8}{5} = 1\frac{3}{5}$ **d.** $\frac{2}{4} \times 6 = \frac{12}{4} = \frac{6}{2} = 3$

Pages 20–21: Percentages

$\frac{1}{2}$=50%=0.5 $\frac{3}{4}$=75%=0.75 $\frac{2}{5}$=40%=0.4 $\frac{4}{5}$=80%=0.8 $\frac{1}{10}$=10%=0.1
$\frac{1}{25}$, 0.25, 30%, 0.6, $\frac{8}{10}$

a. 30% **b.** $\frac{1}{5}$ **c.** 0.4 **d.** Sadie by 5% or $\frac{1}{20}$ or 0.05 **e.** $\frac{3}{20}$ **f.** 50%

Pages 22–23: Shapes

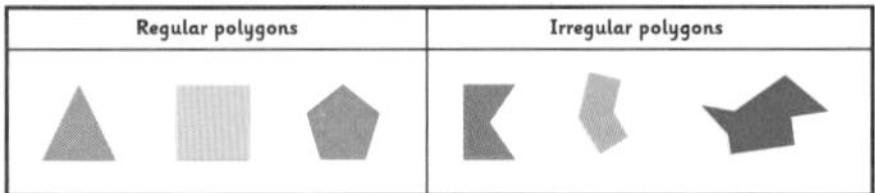

(In a regular shape, all sides will be the same length and all of the angles will be the same. Irregular shapes have lengths and angles of different measurements.)
a. No, it needs 3 equal sides. **b.** No, it also needs equal sides. **c.** All sides should be equal. All angles should be equal.

Hexagonal prism: 6 rectangular faces, 2 hexagonal faces, 12 vertices, 18 edges
Square-based pyramid: 1 square face, 4 triangular faces, 5 vertices, 8 edges
Triangular prism: 3 rectangular faces, 2 triangular faces, 6 vertices, 9 edges
Cylinder: 2 circular faces, 1 curved face, 0 vertices, 2 edges
Cuboid: 6 rectangular faces, 3 pairs of equal faces, 8 vertices, 12 edges
Triangular-based pyramid: 4 triangular faces, 4 vertices, 6 edges

Pages 24–25: Angles

a. 55° b. 80° c. 80°

Natalie faces the start again first.

d. 160°   e. 90°   f. 188°   g. 175°   h. 112°

Pages 26–27: Imperial measures

Butter - 1 pound - 480g
Self raising flour - 8oz - 240g
Caster sugar - 6oz - 180g
Raisins - 4oz - 120g
Cherries - 2oz - 60g

Half a pint of milk is 284ml (because it is half of 568ml)
a. < **b.** > **c.** < **d.** < **e.** base: 15cm / lid: 10cm
3 feet and 90cm / 4 inches and 10cm / $1\frac{1}{2}$ feet and 0.45m
f. 1 litre   **g.** 3 inches   **h.** 1 metre   **i.** 20 ounces   **j.** 1kg

Pages 28–29: Perimeter and area

a. 390m² (3)   b. 600m² (5)   c. 230m² (2)   d. 144m² (1)   e. 500m² (4)

Area of oval: approximately 126m² *(answer may vary)*

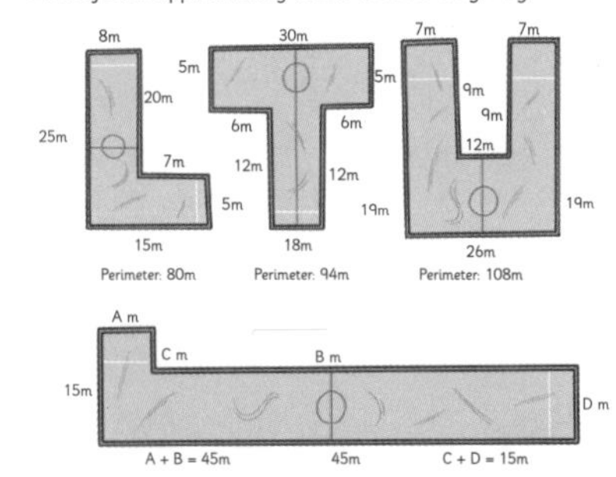

Pages 30–31: Line graphs

a. 4 metres b. 5 minutes between 5–10 minutes and 5 minutes between 35–40 minutes, so 10 minutes in total c. 6 metres d. 20 minutes e. 15 minutes f. Martha's g. 2 metres h. 5 minutes i. Martha's. The difference is 5 minutes.